NEW YORK
The Empire State

★

TEN TOP FACTS ABOUT NEW YORK

★ ★ ★ ★ ★ ★ ★ ★ ★ ★ ★ ★ ★

- State nickname: **The Empire State**

- State motto: ***Excelsior*** **(Latin for "Ever upward")**

- Capital: **Albany**

- Area: **49,576 square miles**

- State flower: **Rose**

- State tree: **Sugar maple**

- State bird: **Bluebird**

- State animal: **Beaver**

- State fish: **Brook trout**

- State song: **"I Love New York" (words and music by Steve Karmen)**

For Ian and Amanda, native New Yorkers and proud of it!

Photo credits:

p. 4: U.S. Mint; p. 5: (top left) Superstock Images, Jacksonville, FL, (bottom left) North Wind Picture Archives, Alfred, ME, (top right) North Wind Picture Archives; p. 6: (both) North Wind Picture Archives; p. 7: Brown Brothers, Sterling, PA; p. 8: (left and top right) North Wind Picture Archives, (bottom right) Superstock Images; p. 9: (top right) Bettmann/Corbis, New York, NY, (bottom right) North Wind Picture Archives; p. 10: Bettmann/Corbis; p. 11: (left) North Wind Picture Archives, (right) Superstock Images; p. 12: (top left) Brown Brothers, (others) North Wind Picture Archives; p. 13: (top) Brown Brothers, (right) Underwood & Underwood/Bettmann/Corbis; p. 14: (top) Brown Brothers, (others) Superstock Images; p. 15: (top) J. Dominis, TimePix, New York, NY, (bottom right) Bettmann/Corbis; p. 16: (both) New York State Department of Economic Development, Albany, NY; p. 17: Superstock Images; p. 18: (top left) Ted Thai/TimePix, (top right) © John Eastcott/Image works/Woodstock, NY, (center right) Superstock Images; p. 19: (left) Superstock Images, (right) New York State Dept. of Economic Development; p. 20 (left) G. Mooney/Corbis, (top right) New York State Dept. of Economic Development, (center right) R. Estall/Corbis; p. 21 (top left) M. S. Yamashita/Corbis, (bottom left) Don Kelly Photography, Mays Landing, NJ, (right) Superstock Images; p. 22: (top left) Lee Snider/Corbis, (bottom left) Superstock Images, (right) Women's Rights National Historical Park, Seneca Falls, NY; p. 23: Brown Brothers (Eastman, Gehrig, Howe), Paul Morse/Corbis (Abdul-Jabbar); p. 24: Corbis/Bettmann (LaGuardia, Sagoyewatha), Superstock Images (Roosevelt, Salk); p. 25: Pacha/Corbis (Streisand), New York State Dept. of Economic Development (Truth), Superstock Images (Whitman); p. 26: Brown Brothers.

Photo research by Dwayne Howard

All other illustrations by John Speirs

ISBN 0-439-22301-6

THE
Jim Henson
—COMPANY—

12 11 10 9 8 7 6 5 4 3 2 1   1 2 3 4 5/0

Designed by Madalina Stefan

Printed in the U.S.A.

First Scholastic printing, July 2001

NEW YORK
The Empire State

By Nancy Krulik

SCHOLASTIC INC.

New York Toronto London Auckland Sydney Mexico City New Delhi Hong Kong

A Celebration of the Fifty States

★ ★ ★ ★ ★ ★ ★ ★ ★ ★ ★ ★

In January 1999, the U.S. Mint started an ambitious ten-year program to commemorate each of the fifty United States. Over the next several years (through 2008), they will issue five newly designed quarters each year.

One side (obverse) of each new quarter will display the profile of George Washington and the words *Liberty, In God We Trust,* and *United States of America.* The other side (reverse) will feature a design honoring a specific state's unique history, the year it became a state, the year of the quarter's issue, and the words *E Pluribus Unum* (Latin for "From many, one"). The quarters are being issued in the order in which the states joined the Union, beginning with the thirteen original colonies.

To find out more about the 50 State Quarters™ Program, visit the official U.S. Mint Web site at *www.USMINT.gov.*

NEW YORK'S QUARTER: The Gateway to Freedom

Give me your tired, your poor,
Your huddled masses yearning to breathe free,
The wretched refuse of your teeming shore.
Send these, the homeless, tempest-tost to me.
I lift my lamp beside the golden door!

—*from "The New Colossus" by Emma Lazarus, engraved on the base of the Statue of Liberty*

For centuries, New York has been the point of arrival for millions of immigrants in search of the American dream. Whether those immigrants arrived by boat, as many did during the 1800s, or by plane, as they do today, New York is the first place where they set foot on American soil.

The New York quarter proudly heralds the state's heritage as a port of welcome with the words *Gateway to Freedom.* The Statue of Liberty, whose torch has lit the way to freedom for so many new Americans, stands in the foreground against an outline of the state. The Erie Canal, a massive waterway that connected New York's eastern coast with the northern part of the state near the Great Lakes, is also clearly shown, indicating the importance of the canal in New York's—and the nation's—history.

Iroquois building fortifications

Algonquin longhouses on Manhattan Island, 16th century

In the Beginning

Long before European settlers reached the shores of what we now call New York State, the land was home to many Native American tribes. The Algonquins occupied much of the area we call the Hudson Valley, Manhattan, and Long Island. The rest of the state was home to the member tribes of the Iroquois League, including the Cayuga, Mohawk, Oneida, Onondaga, and Seneca tribes. (The Tuscarora tribe joined the Iroquois League's confederation in 1722.)

Giovanni da Verrazano is believed to have first sailed into New York's bay in 1524. Hired by King Francis I of France, he was sent to explore North America. In 1609, an Englishman named Henry Hudson, who was hired by the Dutch to seek out

Henry Hudson

a northwest passage to Asia, followed da Verrazano's lead and sailed into the river that now bears Hudson's name.

In 1614, the Dutch established their first settlement in the region, Fort Nassau, which is located near present-day Albany. In 1621, the Dutch West India Company, a group of Dutch merchants, was given permission to establish a colony known as New Netherland, named after their homeland. The families of thirty employees of the Dutch-West India Company immigrated to the colony.

One of these new residents was a man named Peter Minuit. He and a group of Dutch colonists built a fort in the area we now know as Manhattan. Peter Minuit purchased the land from the local Native Americans for goods worth about sixty Dutch guilders (twenty-four American dollars). The Dutch settlers who took over the land called their home New Amsterdam.

While the Dutch were settling along the Hudson River and in Manhattan, British colonists from Connecticut and

Peter Minuit purchases Manhattan

Massachusetts were making their way south to settlements on Long Island and Manhattan. For a while, Dutch and British citizens lived peacefully side by side. In 1664, King Charles II of England gave his brother James, the Duke of York, a charter to set up a new colony in the region. The British sent a huge fleet of ships into what is known today as New York Harbor. Peter Stuyvesant, the Dutch

French and Indian attack on Schenectady, New York

governor, knew his colonists would be outnumbered by the British and surrendered New Amsterdam without a fight. The British renamed the colony New York as a tribute to the Duke of York.

In 1669, the French began settling the Niagara region of Canada. They built a fortress on Lake Champlain, then tried to take over parts of northern New York. The British did not want to give up their land and war soon broke out.

From 1689 through 1763, New Yorkers suffered through four wars between the French and the British. The last was the French and Indian War, also known as the Seven Years' War. Throughout the course of the battles, the French received help from the Algonquin tribe, while the British sought aid from the Iroquois. The fighting ended with the Treaty of Paris, which was signed in 1763.

Revolution!

By the mid–1700s, many New Yorkers were tiring of British government rule over their colony. They were angered by the ever-present British troops and were resistant to the rulings of British judges. They were especially furious about the series of taxes imposed upon them by the British.

The frustration over taxation without representation came to a head in 1773 when the British Parliament imposed a tea tax. In protest, a group of Massachusetts colonists dropped 340 chests of tea into Boston Harbor. That act of rebellion, the Boston Tea Party, unified all the colonies in their fight against England. Representatives from New York and the other colonies showed their support of the Boston colonists by denouncing Britain's restrictions and taxes at the meeting of the First Continental Congress in 1774.

In New York State, the struggle for independence began even before the colonies officially declared themselves independent from England. In 1775, Ethan Allen led a group of patriots called the Green Mountain Boys into Fort Ticonderoga, a British-held fortress near Lake Champlain. The Green Mountain Boys sneaked into the fort under cover of night. They surprised the sleeping British soldiers and demanded their surrender.

Ethan Allen and the Green Mountain Boys managed to capture Fort Ticonderoga from the British without firing a single shot. They then took the cannons and mortars from the fort and brought them to American troops in New England. These new arms gave General George Washington, leader of the Continental army, the power he needed

The capture of Fort Ticonderoga

to force the British to leave Boston Harbor.

On July 4, 1776, the Second Continental Congress declared the colonies independent from Britain. Many colonists supported independence, but not all New Yorkers were in favor of losing the protection of the British government. In fact, after the Declaration of Independence was approved by New York's provincial congress on July 9, 1776, many New York loyalists refused to join the patriot forces, choosing instead to fight alongside the British. Some of these "Tories," as they were called, convinced the Iroquois to fight against the patriots. In retaliation, General Washington sent federal troops to fight the Iroquois in 1779. Troops led by General James Clinton and General John Sullivan raided villages, killed the Native

Destruction of Indian villages by federal troops

Americans' livestock, and burned their fields. The Iroquois were forced off their land and retreated north to Canada. After the war, those who remained were forced to give up their land and live on reservations.

Nearly one-third of the battles during the Revolutionary War were fought in New York. Although General Washington lost his first battle in New York City in

Battle of Saratoga

August 1776, the patriots went on to score a decisive win in the Battle of Saratoga in October 1777. The war ended in 1783, and in 1785, New York City became the temporary capital of the newly formed United States of America.

Over the next few years, representatives from the thirteen colonies worked together to draw up a governing document—the Constitution of the United States. In July 1788, New York ratified the U.S. Constitution and became the eleventh state to join the Union. In 1789, George Washington was inaugurated as the first President of the United States in New York City's Federal Hall. The city served as the new nation's capital until 1790.

George Washington arriving in Manhattan for his inauguration

The Fighting Continues

Even after the treaty ending the war was signed in 1783, the troubles with the British were not over. Britain was engaged in a war with France over maritime rights. In need of sailors to man their naval ships, the British captured American sailors, claiming they were deserters, and forced them to serve in Britain's military. On June 18, 1812, President James Madison signed a declaration of war against the British.

Much of the fighting of the War of 1812 took place near the New York-Canada border. The Americans lost many of the early battles of the war, but in 1814, they won major battles near the Chesapeake Bay in Maryland, and along Lake Champlain in New York. The British were forced to admit defeat and agreed to a peace treaty, the Treaty of Ghent, which was signed on December 24, 1814.

Making Connections

As the British removed their troops from the Great Lakes region, pioneers began to settle northern and western New York. By 1820, New York had a population of more than 1,370,000, making it the most populated of any state. Settlers in northern and western New York needed food and supplies that could best be provided by their fellow New Yorkers along the Atlantic Coast. At the same time, the easterners were anxious to benefit from the growing bounty in the western part of New York. Shipping goods back and forth

DeWitt Clinton pouring water from Lake Erie into the Atlantic Ocean

between the two sections of the state, however, was costly and time-consuming.

In 1817, New York governor DeWitt Clinton convinced the state legislature to support the building of a canal linking the Hudson River and the Atlantic Ocean to the Great Lakes. The Erie Canal, which is 363 miles long, 40 feet wide, and 4 feet deep, took eight years to complete. Nicknamed "Clinton's Ditch" by those who opposed its construction, the Erie Canal cost nearly seven million dollars to build and few people believed it could ever earn back that cost.

Despite these initial criticisms, the canal cut travel time in half and shipping costs dropped nearly ninety-five percent throughout the state. By 1840, New York City was the busiest port in the nation. And in 1831, New York's first railway opened, connecting Albany and Schenectady, making the transport of goods even faster and less expensive.

Opening of the Erie Canal

New Freedoms

Until 1839, New York was controlled mainly by wealthy merchants and real estate owners. Farmers were forced to rent farmland from landowners, who were able to set their own prices. Certain tenant farmers throughout the state refused to pay what they viewed as excessive rent to the heirs of Stephen Van Rensselaer, a major landlord in Albany County. In protest, the tenants fought the Van Rensselaer family's attempts to close down their farms in what became known as the Antirent War. In 1845, after a sheriff was killed, the governor called out the militia to stop the battles between renters and landowners. Finally, in 1846, the state passed a law allowing farmers the opportunity to own the land they farmed. New York's most powerful landlords began breaking up their huge estates and dividing them into small independent farms.

Voting laws were changing, too. By the 1820s, although women and people of color could not vote at all, white men no longer had to own land to be able to vote. And by 1846, the state's new constitution decreed that major state officials had to be elected by the people, rather than appointed by committee.

As New York inched closer to becoming a more democratic state, many citizens supported the antislavery cause. Just because New York was a northern state, however, did not mean that every citizen was opposed to slavery. While many New Yorkers proudly joined the Union forces during the Civil War (which began in 1861), others were not so willing. In fact, in July 1863, proslavery New Yorkers and the state's poorest citizens gathered in New York City to protest the draft. Drafted men were allowed to hire substitutes to serve in their place for a sum of $300. However, this provision did not help poor individuals. Riots broke out throughout the city. Angry mobs killed or injured many people, and destroyed more than one million dollars' worth of property. In the end, troops had to be called in from the Civil War battlefields to stop the rioting.

Although no major Civil War battles took place in New York, the state did send 500,000 troops to fight in the Union army. Fifty thousand New Yorkers died in the Civil War.

Draft riots in New York City, 1863

Facts about the Statue of Liberty

Inauguration celebration, October 28, 1886

Along with the American flag, the Statue of Liberty is one of the United States' best-known symbols of freedom. Standing tall in New York Harbor, she has welcomed thousands of immigrants to our nation. Here are some interesting facts about Lady Liberty:

- The statue's official name is Liberty Enlightening the World.
- The statue was a gift from the people of France to the people of the United States. It also served as a means of heightening interest in trade between the two nations.
- Frédéric-Auguste Bartholdi sculpted the statue.
- Its structural engineer was Gustave Eiffel, who engineered the Eiffel Tower in Paris.
- The Statue of Liberty was completed in early 1885. Once it was finished it was dismantled into 350 individual pieces, loaded into 214 crates, and shipped to the United States.
- The height of the Statue of Liberty from pedestal to torch is 305 feet, one inch—the tallest metal statue ever constructed.
- The statue's total weight is 225 tons.
- The seven spikes in Miss Liberty's crown represent the seven seas and the seven continents of the world. The 25 windows represent the natural minerals of the earth.
- The chains beneath her feet represent Liberty crushing the chains of slavery.
- The statue's left hand, in which she holds her tablet, is 16 feet, five inches long. Her index finger is eight feet long.
- In 1999, Liberty Island was actually proclaimed part of New Jersey.

Factory in Buffalo

New York City, 1880s

The Growth of the Empire State

After the Civil War ended in 1865, New York's economy boomed. Factories sprung up around the state, particularly in Buffalo—the state's connection to the developing west. New York City also continued to grow as the nation's leading industrial, financial, and cultural center. European immigrants, eager for work in New York's factories, flooded the state. By 1900, more than seven million people proudly called themselves New Yorkers.

Immigrants on Ellis Island, 1901

Sewing room sweatshop, 1910

Many of those new immigrants found employment in dark, poorly ventilated clothing factories known as sweatshops. Immigrant laborers in the sweatshops were often paid low wages and forced to work long hours without adequate breaks. Some factory owners did not even allow talking in the workplace.

The conditions in these sweatshops were not only harsh, they were dangerous. In 1911, New York City's Triangle Shirtwaist Company went up in flames. One hundred forty-six workers (mostly Italian and Jewish women and girls) were killed in the fire because the building had no fire escapes and the workers were trapped inside.

This fire led to the imposition of stricter building codes throughout the city and the passage of new protective labor legislation throughout the state. Immigrants continued to work in factories, but they were now able to demand better working conditions, higher pay, and shorter hours.

Triangle Shirtwaist Company fire, 1911

Scene on Wall Street after the stock market crash, 1929

When the United States entered World War I in 1917, New York's factory boom increased. The state provided materials of all kinds to help the war effort. And the port in New York City was busier than ever as thousands of American soldiers departed for Europe.

By 1929, the nation found itself on the brink of the Great Depression. When the stock market crashed, many financiers lost all their money. Production halted in the factories. Former millionaires and factory workers stood side by side, peddling apples in the streets. Franklin D. Roosevelt became New York's governor in 1929 and he established many social programs to help the citizens of his state.

Roosevelt was elected President in 1933 and he turned his attention to helping the entire nation emerge from the Depression. One of Roosevelt's most remarkable programs was the Works

Breadline in New York City

Franklin D. Roosevelt

14

Woodstock Festival, 1969

Progress Administration (WPA), started in 1935. Later renamed the Work Projects Administration, the organization provided $11 billion in work relief to nearly nine million Americans. Many of the WPA's funded projects were cultural programs that provided employment for artists, writers, and musicians.

In 1941, Roosevelt led the country into World War II after the Japanese bombed Pearl Harbor. New York provided more materials for the war effort than any other state and its economy again grew prosperous. Bridges and highways were built, important waterways opened, and the population continued to surge throughout the post-war decades.

Across the country, the 1960s were a time of cultural change and political upheaval. Politically, New York City, like many other urban areas, became the site of civil rights protests and marches. Student protests against the Vietnam War also took place on the campuses of many of the state's colleges. One of the nation's largest antiwar demonstrations took place at Columbia University in New York City.

On the cultural front, New York City's fashion industry influenced the way Americans dressed. The city's famed Broadway theater district became home to radical new musicals such as 1968's *Hair*, which reflected the changing lifestyles of the nation's youth. In 1969, a farm in Bethel, New York, became famous as the site of Woodstock, a three-day celebration of rock and roll.

Hippies in New York City, 1967

15

Albany

New York Today

New York was the nation's leader in industry until the early 1970s, when it fell slightly behind California. The factories in Buffalo specialize in heavy industry; Syracuse produces metals and machinery; Albany, Troy, and Schenectady manufacture paper goods; Binghamton factories produce computers and other business machines; and New York City remains one of the world's leaders in the garment and publishing industries.

Tourism is also a huge source of revenue in New York. Millions of people visit New York City each year, making it one of the top tourist attractions in the world. The rest of the state gets its share of tourists, too. People are attracted to the many parks and campgrounds, as well as mountain ski resorts in the Catskill and Adirondack mountain regions. World-famous Niagara Falls is one of the top honeymoon vacation spots in the country.

New York leads the nation in the banking securities and communications industries. The state is home to 65 Fortune 500 companies, more than any other state. In a single day, more than one trillion dollars in financial trades can take place at the New York Stock Exchange on Wall Street, the indisputable center of the world's financial community.

Although it is not usually acknowledged for its agricultural industry, New York State ranks second in the country in the output of apples. But it isn't the apple trees that give New York City its nickname, the Big Apple. That name was made popular during the 1930s by jazz musicians. Playing in New York City, in particular the theaters of Harlem and Broadway, was considered the ultimate success. When playing outside the city, the musicians were in the branches ("the sticks"); in the city, they were playing the Big Apple. The phrase was not used much in the fifties and sixties but it was revived by the tourist industry in the seventies to attract visitors to the city. Since then, it has become an internationally known nickname.

Legend has it that George Washington gave the state of New York its nickname, the Empire State. In 1783, the first President of the United States predicted that New York would one day become the seat of a great empire. Judging by the vast economic, cultural, and population growth the state has seen throughout its history, it seems fair to say that George Washington's prophecy has come true.

Brooklyn Bridge (foreground)

World Trade Towers

Rose Center for Earth and Space

Elephants performing with trainer

American Museum of Natural History and the Rose Center for Earth and Space

Are you interested in dinosaur bones? Do you want to find out what life was like for ancient Aztecs and early Native Americans? Ever wonder how similar humans are to apes? You will find exhibits relating to all these topics, as well as animal dioramas, minerals and gemstones from around the world, and many other exhibits at this museum on Manhattan's Upper West Side. The museum itself was founded in 1869, but it is constantly adding new exhibit halls. The latest addition is the Rose Center, a state-of-the-art planetarium, and the Cullman Hall of the Universe.

The Catskill Game Farm

Located in the heart of the Catskill Mountains, this 68-year-old farm has more than 2,000 rare animals, representing 150 species from around the world. Take a half-mile train trip and observe hundreds of birds, native to the Catskills area, flying freely in their natural habitat. There is also a petting zoo at the farm, filled with baby animals you can bottle-feed, and animal shows featuring talented four-legged creatures.

Immigration station

Ellis Island Immigration Museum

Between the years 1892 and 1954, more than twelve million immigrants entered the United States via New York Harbor. Today, more than 100 million Americans can trace their roots to Ellis Island, which may explain the popularity of this major tourist attraction. Although Ellis Island no longer functions as a screening center for immigrants, it remains a monument to the people who came to America in search of freedom and a better way of life.

Visitors to the Ellis Island Museum can see the Great Hall, where millions of people waited in line for medical examinations and legal processing—both of which were required before the newcomers could leave the island. There are also photos, family heirlooms, clothing, and jewelry, all of which once belonged to actual immigrants. The American Wall of Honor contains the names of more than half a million immigrants who passed through Ellis Island.

The Empire State Building and the World Trade Center

The 1,224-foot-high (not including its antenna) Empire State Building was completed in 1931 and held the record as the world's tallest building for more than forty years. In 1973, the World Trade Towers, the twin buildings that stand 1,368 and 1,362 feet high, became the tallest buildings in New York City. Today, both the Empire State Building and the World Trade Center remain the most recognizable landmarks in Manhattan's world-famous skyline.

The Empire State Building's tower obser-vatory on the 102nd floor offers spectacular views of the city as well as of neighboring New Jersey and Connecticut. (Some people claim to have seen as far as Massachusetts and Pennsylvania!) The World Trade Center Observatory is located on the 107th floor of 2 World Trade Center. The elevator ride to the top takes only 58 seconds! The view of the Statue of Liberty, Manhattan, New York Harbor, and Brooklyn is spectacular. There is also a helicopter simulation ride and a light show.

Inside Howe Caverns

Howe Caverns

This natural phenomenon was discovered in 1842 in Schoharie County by a farmer named Lester Howe. Ever since Howe stumbled upon the amazing limestone caverns beneath his land, visitors have been touring the ancient rock formations carved over the course of six million years by an underground river. Back in the 1800s, the tour of Howe Caverns lasted eight to ten hours. Visitors had to walk 156 feet down to reach the base and then return to the surface. Today, tourists can take a short elevator ride to view the stalagmites and stalactites. The caverns offer a rare,

Empire State Building

unspoiled view of these natural rock formations. If you visit, bring your sweatshirt—the temperature inside the caverns is fifty-two degrees all year long!

Planes on the *Intrepid*

The Intrepid Sea-Air-Space Museum

Before it became a New York City museum, the aircraft carrier *Intrepid* was on active duty during World War II and the Vietnam War. It also played a part in NASA's space program. Today, the warship is permanently docked in New York City and houses exhibits about the Navy and the space program.

Visitors to the *Intrepid* can view many of the planes and helicopters actually flown in combat by the U.S. military. They can also learn about recent U.S. undersea discoveries and see a model of *Orbiter*, NASA's first space shuttle.

The Iroquois Indian Museum

The Iroquois Indian Museum, located in the Catskill Mountains, is a salute to the mighty Iroquois nation. Visitors can view the largest collection of contemporary Iroquois arts and crafts work in the nation. The museum

Iroquois baskets

also has storytelling and dance presentations. There is a children's area where kids can make corn husk dolls, string beaded necklaces, and pound corn into cornmeal just as the Iroquois used to do.

Genessee River Gorge

Letchworth State Park

The Letchworth State Park in western New York is home to the Genessee River Gorge, also known as the Grand Canyon of the East. The Gorge is seventeen miles around and 600 feet deep. Visitors to the park can hike trails in the gorge itself. The park also contains three waterfalls and is a favorite spot for campers.

Metropolitan Museum of Art

The Metropolitan Museum of Art

Located on Manhattan's famed Fifth Avenue, the Metropolitan Museum of Art boasts one of the largest and finest art collections in the world—more than two million pieces of artwork! There are collections from ancient Greece, Rome, and Egypt, art and sculpture from Africa, Oceania, and the Americas, displays of arms and armor, as well as musical instruments from around the world. The rooftop sculpture garden has a great view of Central Park.

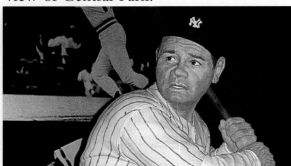
Statue of Babe Ruth in the Baseball Hall of Fame

National Baseball Hall of Fame

For baseball fans, there is no place like Cooperstown, home to the National Baseball Hall of Fame and Museum. The history of our national pastime can be found within the walls of this museum. Exhibits include artifacts from the great home-run chases, including balls hit by Babe Ruth, Roger Maris, Mark McGwire, and Sammy Sosa. The Hall of Fame time line features the bat Mickey Mantle used when he hit his record-breaking 565-foot home run, and the bat Hank Aaron used to slug home run number 714 out of Yankee Stadium, beating Babe Ruth's record.

Niagara Falls

Niagara Falls

Every minute 500,000 tons of water plunge from one level of the Niagara River to the other. Visitors can watch the falls from Niagara Falls State Park, the first state park in the nation, or put on a raincoat and board the *Maid of the Mist*, a boat that tours the falls from the base. Helicopter tours of the falls give tourists a bird's-eye view of this amazing force of nature.

Old Bethpage Village Restoration

Travel back in time to the 1800s in this remodeled Long Island village that occupies 100 acres. Tour

Powell Farm barns at Old Bethpage Village

guides in period costumes take guests through the village—a general store, a blacksmith shop, a one-room school-house, and a church. Just beyond Old Bethpage Village are homes and shops, and the Powell Farm, where cows, sheep, pigs, and horses are still fed and tended.

United Nations

United Nations Headquarters

One hundred eighty-nine national flags—one for each member country—surround the United Nations building, which is located on six blocks along the East River in Manhattan. The United Nations selected New York City as its permanent home in 1946, and the building opened in 1952. Since then, ambassadors from around the world have come to New York to work together to protect human rights and bring peace to the world. Visitors are also welcome to tour the building.

Women's Rights National Historical Park and Museum

The Women's Rights National Historical Park and Museum are located in Seneca Falls, the site of the first women's rights convention in 1848. Visitors can view videos, films, and exhibits that document the history of the women's movement. Guided tours of the home of Elizabeth Cady Stanton are also available. She, along with Lucretia Mott and others, organized that first convention and began the battle for women's voting rights.

Statues of 1848 convention participants

Famous People from New York

George Eastman (1854–1932)

Waterville native George Eastman was a bank clerk with an interest in photography. That hobby became his ticket to fame and fortune when he developed an improved process for making photographic plates. He also introduced flexible film to the marketplace. In 1888, George Eastman perfected the Kodak Box Camera, and within two years more than 10,000 amateur photographers had purchased one! The Eastman Kodak Company went on to create a variety of pocket cameras and roll film, revolutionizing the amateur photography industry.

Julia Ward Howe (1819–1910)

New York City's Julia Ward Howe came to prominence in the years before the Civil War as a reformer and staunch abolitionist. She often wrote editorials for the Boston *Commonwealth*, an antislavery newspaper. Her most famous work—a poem called "The Battle Hymn of the Republic"—appeared in *Atlantic Monthly* magazine in 1862. It was set to music and the song gained huge popularity in the years following the Civil War. Julia Ward Howe continued her work as an activist, fighting for women's rights, until her death in 1910.

Lou Gehrig (1903–1941)

Yankees' baseball legend and New York native Lou Gehrig had a lifetime batting average of .340, played in seven World Series (of which the Yankees won six), hit twenty-three grand slam home runs, and led the American League in home runs for three years. Gehrig's career was cut short, however, when he was diagnosed with amyotrophic lateral sclerosis (ALS), an ailment that eventually caused his death. To this day, the illness is often referred to as Lou Gehrig's disease.

Kareem Abdul-Jabbar (1947–   )

At seven feet two inches tall, Kareem Abdul-Jabbar was a powerful opponent on the basketball court during his years as part of the Los Angeles Lakers team from 1975 to 1989. But his skills were developed on the concrete courts of Harlem during the 1950s and early 1960s. Kareem's list of on-court accomplishments is truly amazing. He is the only player in NBA history to have won the most valuable player award six times. He is one of only fifteen players to have won NBA titles with two teams (the Los Angeles Lakers and the Milwaukee

Bucks), and he was invited to play in a total of eighteen All-Star games.

Fiorello LaGuardia (1882–1947)

Fiorello LaGuardia was a political reformer, a congressman, and the head of the United Nations Relief and Rehabilitation Administration. He was also one of the most popular mayors of New York City during his two terms in office.

During that time he became famous for battling political corruption and improving the city's housing, health, recreation, and arts programs.

Sagoyewatha (1758–1830)

Sagoyewatha, the famous chief of the Seneca tribe, is perhaps best known by his nickname, Red Jacket. During the Revolutionary War, Sagoyewatha was reluctantly drawn into the war on the side of the red-coated British, which is how he received his nickname. He then fought with the Americans during the War of 1812. Sagoyewatha later became an advocate for Native American causes, including the maintenance of a separate Iroquois jurisdiction.

Eleanor Roosevelt (1884–1962)

Eleanor Roosevelt, wife of President Franklin D. Roosevelt, never ran for office, but during her lifetime she managed to bring about tremendous change. Eleanor was a champion of civil and human rights. She defied segregation in the South—in 1939 she sat with blacks during the Southern Conference for Human Welfare in Birmingham, which was against Alabama's segregation laws. That same year she personally arranged for Marian Anderson, a black opera singer, to perform on Easter Sunday at the Lincoln Memorial. In her later years, Eleanor Roosevelt served as the head of the Human Rights Commission for the United Nations, working to gain freedom for people all over the world.

Jonas Salk (1914–1995)

Jonas Salk's parents immigrated to New York City from Russia in the early 1900s. The first member of his family to go to college, Salk attended New York University and studied science and medicine.

In 1955, while working at the University of Pittsburgh Medical School, Dr. Salk created his famous polio vaccine, which virtually wiped out this widespread disease.

Barbra Streisand (1942–)

Brooklyn-born Barbra Streisand is a singer, actress, writer, director, and producer. She won the New York Drama Critics best supporting actress award in 1962 for her role in *I Can Get It for You Wholesale* and received her first Grammy Award the following year for her debut album. She went on to star in *Funny Girl* on Broadway and in the film, winning her first Oscar for her portrayal of fellow New Yorker Fanny Bryce. Barbra Streisand has also directed (and starred in) several films, including *Yentl* and *The Prince of Tides*.

Sojourner Truth (approximately 1797–1883)

Sojourner Truth was born a slave in up-state New York. Her given name was Isabella Baumfree. In 1828, New York freed all its slaves. Isabella, believing she heard God's voice, moved to New York City and began preaching in the streets. In 1843, the voices she heard told her to change her name and travel along the East Coast. Along the way, she discovered the abolitionist movement and began touring the country speaking out against slavery. Soon she took on the cause of women's rights, too. She spent the rest of her life speaking out for equal rights for blacks and women.

Walt Whitman (1819–1892)

Long Island's own Walt Whitman is considered one of the greatest American poets. He started out in the newspaper business, learning the printing trade when he was just eleven years old. He continued in the business as a reporter and editor and, in the late 1830s, became editor in chief of the weekly *Long Islander* newspaper. His most famous poems are included in his book *Leaves of Grass*.

Presidents from New York State

★ ★ ★ ★ ★ ★

Martin Van Buren

(born in Kinderhook)

★

Millard Fillmore

(born in Locke)

★

Theodore Roosevelt

(born in New York City)

★

Franklin Roosevelt

(born at Hyde Park)

The Legend of Sleepy Hollow

By WASHINGTON IRVING

Native New Yorker Washington Irving was one of the most masterful short story writers of his day. Many of his tales remain every bit as popular now as they were when he first wrote them. Like many of Washington Irving's stories, The Legend of Sleepy Hollow *takes place in New York State—in the village of Sleepy Hollow, which lies along the Hudson River. Sleepy Hollow may sound like a name for a calm, quiet town, but according to Irving's story, the town held a dark secret in the form of a headless horseman who roamed the woods at night.*

The following excerpt describes the time a schoolteacher named Ichabod Crane meets the Headless Horseman one night while riding his horse, Gunpowder.

Ichabod, who had no relish for this strange midnight companion . . . now quickened his steed in the hopes of leaving him behind. The stranger, however, quickened his horse to an equal pace. Ichabod pulled up and fell into a walk, thinking to lag behind. The other did the same. His heart began to sink within him; he endeavored to resume his psalm tune, but his parched tongue clove to the roof of his mouth, and he could not utter a stave. There was something in the moody and dogged silence of his pertinacious companion that was mysterious and appalling. It was soon fearfully accounted for. On mounting a rising ground, which brought the figure of his fellow-traveler in relief against the sky, gigantic in height and muffed in a cloak, Ichabod was horror struck on perceiving that he was headless! But his horror was still more increased on observing that the head, which should have rested on his shoulders, was carried before him on the pommel of his saddle! His terror rose in desperation; he rained a shower of kicks and blows upon Gunpowder, hoping by a sudden movement to give his companion the slip; but the spectre started full jump with him. Away then they dashed through thick and thin; stones flying and sparks flashing at every bound. Ichabod's flimsy garments fluttered in the air, as he stretched his long, lanky body away over his horse's head, in the eagerness of his flight. . . .

An opening in the trees now cheered him with the hopes that the Church Bridge was at hand. The wavering reflection of a silver star in the bosom of the brook told him that he was not mistaken. He saw the walls of the church dimly glaring under the trees beyond. . . . "If I can but reach that bridge," thought Ichabod, "I am safe." Just then he heard the black steed panting and blowing close behind him, he even fancied that he felt his hot breath. Another convulsive kick in the ribs, and old Gunpowder sprang upon the bridge; he thundered over the resounding planks; he gained the opposite side; and now Ichabod cast a look behind to see if his pursuer should vanish according to the rule, in a flash of fire and brimstone. Just then he saw the goblin rising in his stirrups and in the very act of hurling his head at him. Ichabod endeavored to dodge the horrible missile, but too late. It encountered his cranium with a tremendous crash. He was tumbled headlong into the dust and Gunpowder, the black steed, and goblin rider, passed by like a whirlwind.

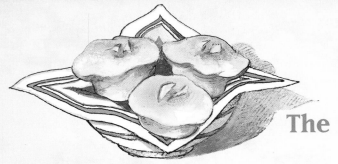

The New York State Muffin

New York is the only state to have an official muffin. This recipe was originally created for the children of the Bear Road Elementary School in North Syracuse. Make sure an adult helps you with the chopping and with using the stove and the oven.

The Official New York State Apple Muffin Recipe

Preheat the oven to 375°F.

Batter

Combine the following dry ingredients and set aside:

2 cups flour
1/2 cup sugar
3/4 cup brown sugar
1/2 teaspoon salt

2 teaspoons baking soda
1/8 teaspoon nutmeg
1 1/2 teaspoons cinnamon
1/2 teaspoon cloves

Combine in a large bowl:

2 cups cored, peeled, and coarsely chopped apples
1/2 cup chopped walnuts
4 ounces cream cheese
1/2 teaspoon vanilla

1/2 cup raisins
3 eggs
1/2 cup melted butter

Add the dry ingredients to the apple mixture a little at a time. Stir until just combined. Do not overmix. Pour the muffin batter into greased or paper-lined muffin tins.

Topping

Combine the following ingredients in a small bowl, then place one to two teaspoons of the mixture on top of each uncooked muffin:

1/2 cup chopped walnuts
1 teaspoon lemon peel
1 teaspoon cinnamon
1/4 cup flour
1/2 cup brown sugar
1 ounce butter, melted

Bake for 25 minutes.
Makes 24 muffins.

What the Mailman Brought

by Carolyn Craven

illustrated by Tomie dePaola

G.P. Putnam's Sons

New York

For M & D and M & M — CC

For Nanette — TdeP

 Published simultaneously in Canada by General Publishing Co. Limited, Toronto.
Printed in Hong Kong by South China Printing Co.
Book design by Nanette Stevenson.

Library of Congress Cataloging-in-Publication Data.
Craven, Carolyn. What the mailman brought.
Summary: While William is sick and unable to go to school, a mysterious mailman brings him unusual packages every day.
[1. Sick—Fiction.] I. dePaola, Tomie, ill.
II. Title. PZ7.C8534Wh 1986 [E] 85-19076
ISBN 0-399-21290-6
First impression

Sunday morning it was raining. William Beauregard had missed the first week of school in his new city, and he was about to miss the second. William was sick. He had started feeling better now, but the doctor had been firm. "You need a lot of rest, my friend," he had said yesterday. "Another week at home, and no running up and down stairs."

William had nothing to do. He had read all his books twice. His train was broken. And he had eaten all the snacks he could eat.

William stared out the window. His old street had front porches, and big lawns, and lots of friends to play with. But William didn't know a single person in the new city. He walked around the room, and then he sat down at his desk. On his largest piece of paper he wrote in big black letters

SICK

He thought a moment. Then he added

OF
THIS

He took his sign to the window and taped it there, so the writing faced out. Maybe someone would see it. Afterward, William climbed in bed and pulled the blankets over his head.

The next morning when William woke up he was surprised to find a big flat parcel on his desk. He ripped off the brown paper and took out three paint-brushes and a palette. Under these was a pad of thick white pebbly paper. And then he found twelve tubes of paint in their own wooden box.

"Real paints!" William whispered. Mr. and Mrs. Beauregard were pleased too.

"I found the package on the doorstep last night," said his mother. "Who do you suppose it's from? I didn't think anyone knew you were sick."

His father brought a jar of water, and then his parents left him to paint.

William sat down at his desk and looked out the window. He saw a row of black iron railings. He saw white lace curtains. He saw grey chimneys. It was Monday morning, and no one was on the street.

Suddenly a figure came around the corner. It was the mailman. Or it looked like the mailman, wearing a blue uniform and pushing a little brown cart. But there was something funny about him. William shut his eyes for a minute, but when he opened them, the mailman looked just as strange. In fact, William thought, he looked very much like a . . .

All at once William remembered his paints. He squeezed out blobs onto the palette and dipped his brush. And he began to paint as the mailman waddled from mailbox to mailbox.

It was late afternoon when his father came upstairs.

"Will, what a great picture," his father said. "Where did you get the idea for it?"

Just then his mother came home from work and ran upstairs too.

"William, another package has come for you. It's marked FRAGILE in big red letters."

William opened the cardboard box and dug through crumpled tissue paper. Under it all was an enormous pale blue egg, smooth and hard and faintly speckled. All three Beauregards gasped.

"What kind of egg could it be?"

"Who could have sent it?"

William said nothing. He was thinking hard. He looked over at his picture. He looked at his egg.

"I think the mailman laid it," he said.

"The mailman *what?*"

"The mailman left it," William said quickly.

"Of course, Will," his father said. "But . . ."

Mrs. Beauregard got up and stroked his head. "I'll bring up your dinner, dear, since the doctor said no stairs."

The next day at eleven, William sat down at his desk. It was still raining, and the street was greyer than ever.

Then something caught his eye.

It was the mailman. Or was it? His nose was long and green and scaly, and he seemed to have a lot of pointed teeth. William was glad he was on the third floor. He painted fast and finished just as the mailman turned the corner and disappeared. He taped the painting up and crawled into bed.

Just before dinnertime, Mrs. Beauregard came up to his room with a box.

"William, another one!" she said.

William pulled it open and took out a shirt. It was covered with purple palm trees. "'See Sunny Florida,'" William read from large letters across the back.

"Nana's the only person we know in Florida," murmured his mother. "But she hates purple."

William thought. Then he looked up.

"Do alligators live in Florida?"

"Yes, in the swamps. Why do you ask?"

But William didn't say anything, and soon his mother went downstairs.

Even before William had opened his eyes on Wednesday morning, he knew it was still raining. But when he put on his new shirt, he felt more cheerful. He ate the breakfast his father brought up and squeezed new paint onto his palette.

The mailman came around the corner waving a long and furry tail. It was striped black and white. William made sure his window was closed tight. Then he started to paint.

When Mr. and Mrs. Beauregard came upstairs that evening with the next package, he was reading in bed.

"William, it's not fair," his father said. "You get all the surprises."

"I'm a little worried about what *he's* left me," said William as he slowly untied the string.

"What *who's* left you?"

William didn't answer.

"Flowers!" his mother cried. "But where are they from?"

William sniffed. "Mmmmm. Do you like my painting?" he asked her.

She untaped it from the window. "Well, it's very nice. Let's go find a vase," she said to his father.

Out in the hall she lowered her voice. "Wallace, I'm a little worried about William. He paints such strange pictures and he won't answer my questions anymore."

"I'll have a talk with him tomorrow," his father said.

Mr. Beauregard went up to see William just before eleven the next day. The two of them looked out at the wet street.

"Well, Will, what are you painting today?"

"The mailman," William said.

His father stood up and walked around the room. "Will, do these animals in your pictures ever frighten you?"

William saw the mailman slide around the corner. "Of course not. They're very friendly."

His father patted his shoulder. "Don't tire yourself out," he said, and went down to his study.

Under the mailman's cap, William saw a shiny silver face. It had round eyes that didn't blink. William took his time painting. "This one is the best," he thought.

William's mother came upstairs at dinnertime carrying an omelette and a heavy box. They opened it together. William lifted out a spiky, spiraled shell. It was a deep rose color, fading to the most delicate pink.

William held it to his ear and heard a roar like the ocean. "It's a conch," his mother said, and stared at it thoughtfully. "I just don't understand," she finally said as she left.

Friday morning William laughed when a fat and furry mailman came into sight. William began to paint as the mailman slowly wriggled himself through the drizzle to the mailboxes. The picture was even better than the last one.

That evening both his parents came upstairs and sat on his bed. There was no box.

"Your doctor's appointment is at ten forty-five, Will," his father said. "Maybe he'll have good news." He reached in his pocket. "Your mother almost missed this one. It had rolled off the front step."

Mr. Beauregard handed him what looked like a plain cotton ball. All three of them stared at it lying in William's palm.

Suddenly William jumped.

"It moved!" he cried.

"Be careful!" his mother said.

As they watched, the cotton ball began to crack down the middle. Something inside was pushing it apart. It seemed to take forever.

"It's a cocoon, and it's hatching," whispered Mr. Beauregard. Presently the butterfly pulled its way out and clung to William's finger. They watched the wings take color as the butterfly slowly waved them dry.

"Let her crawl onto a pencil so you can go to bed, Will," his father said.

Settled in his bed, William wondered what would arrive tomorrow. Suddenly he remembered tomorrow was Saturday, and he had a doctor's appointment. He would miss the mailman, he thought sadly.

"We're having a picnic!" said William's mother on their way home from the doctor's the next day. When they arrived, Mr. Beauregard was already spreading a blanket on the little terrace. The air smelled fresh and wet, and sunshine had begun to dry the puddles.

"What's the news, William?" his father asked.

"School on Monday," he answered. "I'm all better. Let's eat!"

William was halfway through his chocolate when he remembered.

"Did the mailman come?" he asked.

"Yes—as a matter of fact we had a chat. He's been out sick all week, just like you. And sorry, Will, he didn't bring any packages."

"The other ones came later in the day, though," said Mrs. Beauregard.

"I don't think there will be one today," William said. "Yesterday was the last."

They looked at him.

"How do you know, Will?" asked Mr. Beauregard.

"Just a feeling," said William. He was watching a big red butterfly float over their heads toward the south. William waved at the fluttery wings. "Can I wear my purple shirt to school on Monday?"

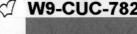

Febold
Feboldson
ARIANE DEWEY

GREENWILLOW BOOKS NEW YORK

FOR EDDIE KOUFLIE

Library of Congress Cataloging in Publication Data
Dewey, Ariane.   Febold Feboldson.
Summary: The Nebraska farmer conquers
cyclones, blizzards, fog, and
grasshoppers in incredible ways.
1. Feboldson, Febold (Legendary character) —
Juvenile literature.   [1. Feboldson,
Febold (Legendary character)   2.Folklore —
United States.   3. Tall tales]   I. Title.
PZ8.1.D54Fe 1984   398.2'2'0973 [E]
83-14222   ISBN 0-688-02533-1
ISBN 0-688-02534-X (lib. bdg.)

CONTENTS

The Year the Snow Wouldn't Melt   5

The Year of the Big Rain   12

The Year of the Striped Weather   17

The Year of the Cyclones   22

The Year of the Great Heat   27

The Year of the Fog   32

The Year of the Grasshoppers   38

THE YEAR THE SNOW
WOULDN'T MELT

Febold Feboldson was the first farmer to come to the Great Plains. He settled in what is now Nebraska.

He liked it fine, except for the weather. There were floods, blizzards, and heat waves, all on the same day. Cyclones whirled dust back and forth from the Rocky Mountains to the Mississippi River.

Other settlers came, but they didn't stay. Febold stayed. It didn't take him long to figure out how to deal with the weather.

7

One year the snow froze so hard, it didn't even melt when summer came. The year was 1848. That was the year gold was discovered in California. Fishermen, firemen, butchers, carpenters, people from the city and people from the country left their work and headed west.

"We're miners now," they shouted.

But the Gold Rush was held up. The snow lay in drifts forty feet high. The miners couldn't cross the plains.

But Febold could.

9

He drove his wagon to Death Valley and loaded it with desert sand.

Desert sand never cools off.

He sold it to the miners. They used it to melt the snow.

And that is how the miners got to California in time to be called forty-niners.

11

THE YEAR
OF THE BIG RAIN

The year started out dry. And it got drier and hotter, hotter and drier. The streams dried up. Febold couldn't go fishing.

"Now that's enough!" he said.

A frog was sitting nearby. Febold splashed it with water from a bucket.

"It's raining!" Febold shouted.

13

The frog croaked the news to his friends.
Soon all the frogs on the prairie were
croaking, "Rain! Rain!" They made such
a din, it sounded like thunder.

Some clouds in the north heard it.
"Thunder!" they cried, and hurried south.
They didn't want to miss the storm.

15

It rained so hard that the frogs were washed down to the Gulf of Mexico. It took them nine months to hop back.

THE YEAR
OF THE STRIPED WEATHER

The sun shone on Febold's cornfield. At
the same time the rain fell on his cane field,
which was just up the hill.

17

The sun was so hot that the corn popped.

It rained so hard the sugar washed out of the cane stalks.

The syrup ran down into the cornfield.
It swept the popcorn into balls. They
were huge.
"Those look good enough to eat," said
Febold.
And he ate them all winter long.

21

THE YEAR
OF THE CYCLONES

At last someone settled near Febold.
His name was Eldad Johnson.
"Does the wind always blow like this?"
he asked.
"No," Febold replied. "Sometimes it
blows harder."

One calm afternoon, Eldad Johnson's grandfather climbed up their windmill to oil the gears. Just then a cyclone whirled by. It blew the old man off the windmill.

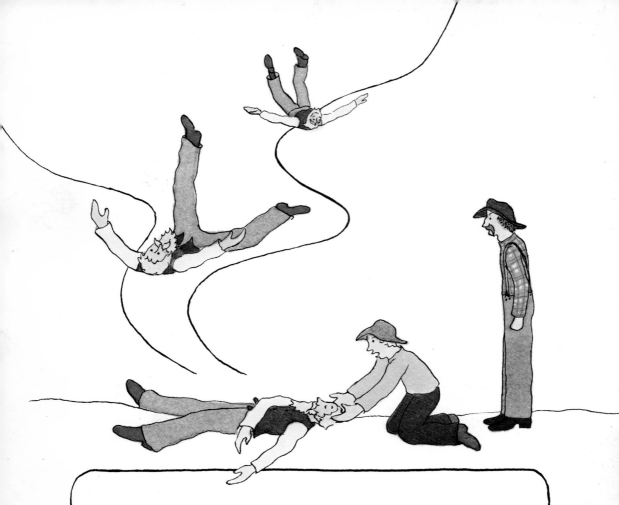

It dropped him flat on his back. All the
breath was knocked out of him.
Eldad and Febold thought he was dead.
Febold built a coffin for him. They dug
his grave near the Dismal River.

Suddenly another cyclone spun up. It blew
the coffin away. Eldad's grandfather fell out.
The storm blew the breath right back into
him. It dropped him on his windmill.

When Eldad got home, there was his grandfather. "Wind sure is fierce today," the old man said.

THE YEAR
OF THE GREAT HEAT

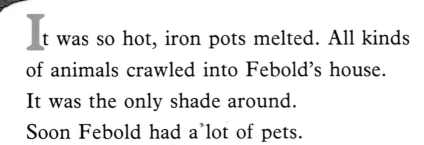

It was so hot, iron pots melted. All kinds of animals crawled into Febold's house.
It was the only shade around.
Soon Febold had a lot of pets.

27

Peggy was a three-legged cat. Febold made a
wooden leg for her. She used it to club rats.

Lizzie was Febold's pet gopher. She dug tunnels under the house. Febold plugged them up, to trap the heat inside. He wanted to save some in case winter ever came back.

30

Then there was a rattlesnake named
Arabella. She rattled her tail at six o'clock
every morning. She made such a racket,
it always woke Febold up. That made him
so mad, he jumped right out of bed.
Arabella was a very reliable alarm clock.

THE YEAR
OF THE FOG

One day the sky began to hiss. It hissed louder and louder.

"What's that?" asked Eldad Johnson.

"Fog's coming," said Febold. "I'd better order some fog-cutters."

"I don't see any fog," complained Eldad.

"You don't now, but you will soon," Febold said.

The air was so hot, the rain turned to steam ten miles up. That's what caused the hissing.

When the steam cooled, it turned into fog. The fog settled on everything. It was so thick Febold had to hold the fog open so Eldad could step through.

Ranchers didn't have to water their herds. The cattle just drank the fog. Pigs rooted around in it. Plants grew down to the sunlight on the other side of the earth.

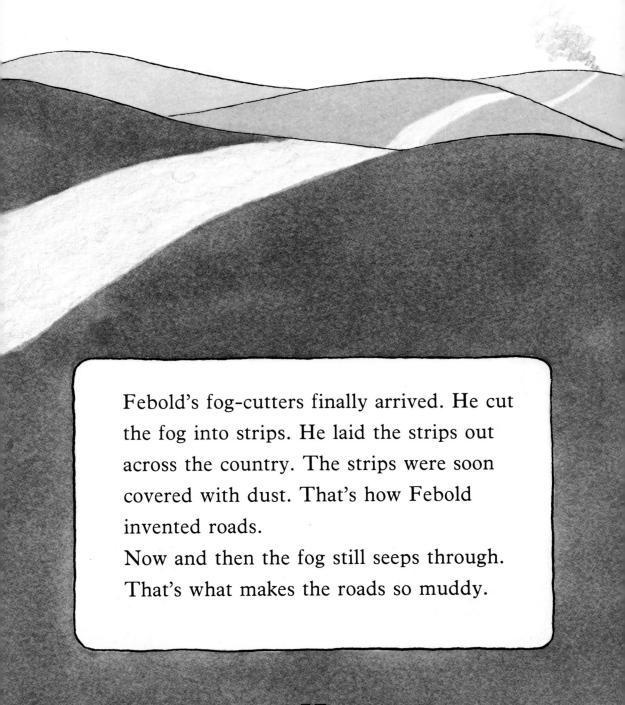

Febold's fog-cutters finally arrived. He cut
the fog into strips. He laid the strips out
across the country. The strips were soon
covered with dust. That's how Febold
invented roads.

Now and then the fog still seeps through.
That's what makes the roads so muddy.

THE YEAR
OF THE GRASSHOPPERS

Every few years grasshoppers swarmed across the plains. One year the grass hoppers ate everything in sight. They ate the crops. They ate the buffalo grass. They ate Febold's popcorn balls. There was nothing left.

Febold wrote to his aunt in New England.
He ordered a hundred hungry turkeys.
But when he let the turkeys loose, the
grasshoppers attacked them.

The hoppers chewed turkey feathers till the turkeys were bare. The birds were so upset, they ran all the way back to Massachusetts.

The grasshoppers were thicker than ever.
Febold swept them into sacks. They ate
right through them.

Febold was furious. He grabbed a handful of hoppers and tried to drown them in the Dismal River. The fish gobbled them up.

43

"By Golly!" said Febold. "Why didn't I think
of fish before?"
He imported enough flying fish to fill a
prairie schooner. They swooped and soared
over the plains.

"Watch 'em catch those pests!" Febold
shouted to Eldad.
When there were no grasshoppers left,
the fish flew back to the sea.

"What a place," Febold said to Eldad. "We're blown about by cyclones. We're frozen by blizzards. We're choked by dust. We're blinded by fog.

"There's no rain and the crops die. Or there's too much rain and the floods wash the crops away. If the floods don't get them, the grasshoppers do.

47

"But the weather can't beat me. It suits me fine."

48